Cover illustration: A German Leopard A1A1 main battle tank.

8

1. A Chinook helicopter hovers overhead as a line of M60A1s move off during Exercise 'Spearpoint '80'. The M60A1 and A2 use the same engine type, the Continental AVDS-1790-2A 12-cylinder air-cooled diesel developing 750bhp at 2,400rpm. The maximum road speed of the M60 is 48.2km/hr and its maximum road range is 500km. The combat weight of the vehicle is 48.9 tonnes. It has a four-man crew.

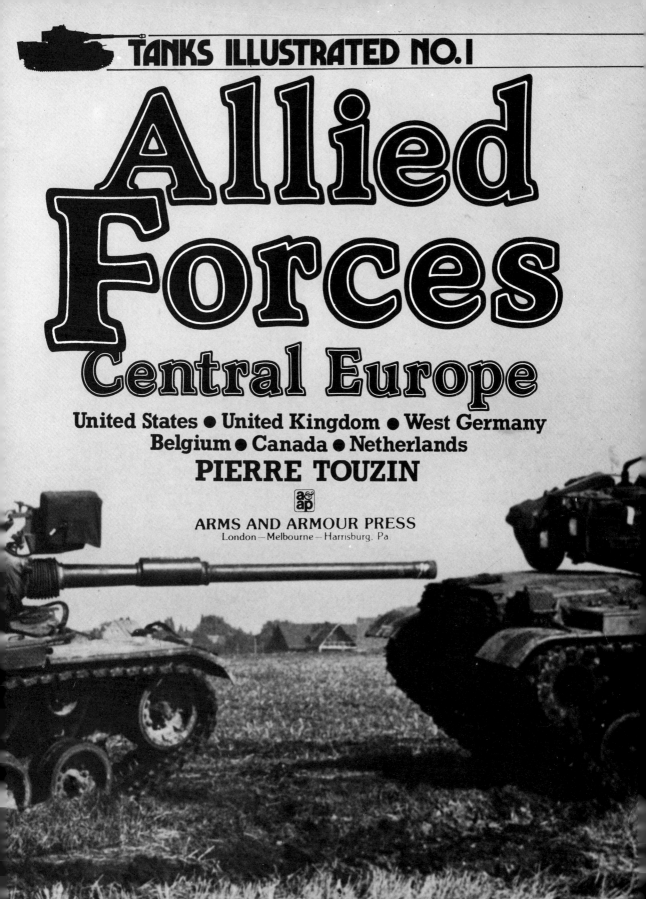

Allied Forces
Central Europe

United States ● United Kingdom ● West Germany
Belgium ● Canada ● Netherlands

PIERRE TOUZIN

a&ap

ARMS AND ARMOUR PRESS
London — Melbourne — Harrisburg, Pa

Introduction

Tanks Illustrated 1: Allied Forces Central Europe
Published in 1983 by
Arms and Armour Press, Lionel Leventhal Limited,
2-6 Hampstead High Street, London NW3 1QQ;
4-12 Tattersalls Lane, Melbourne, Victoria 3000,
Australia; Cameron and Kelker Streets, P.O. Box 1831,
Harrisburg, Pennsylvania 17105, USA

British Library Cataloguing in Publication Data:
Touzin, Pierre
Allied Forces Central Europe. – (Tanks illustrated; 1)
1. North Atlantic Treaty Organization – Pictorial
works   2. Arms and armour – Pictorial works
3. Tanks (Military science) – Pictorial works
I. Title   II. Series
623.74'75'091821   UG446.5
ISBN 0-85368-582-7

Layout by Anthony A. Evans.
Printed in Great Britain by William Clowes,
Beccles, Limited.

The combat units of the NATO forces are in training either separately or together all year round. Much of the training of the ground forces takes place in military camps, but in September each year there is a large-scale exercise in West Germany as part of the 'Autumn Forge' series of exercises. During this time the combat vehicles may be seen outside their usual confines, operating in what would be their environment in a time of conflict. The exercise allows units from the participating nations to familiarize themselves with their allies' items of equipment and to ameliorate problems arising from language difficulties.

This volume presents the main combat vehicle types in use with the major armies protecting NATO's central front: namely units from the Belgian, British, Canadian, Dutch, West German and US armies. The vehicles are depicted on exercise, which provides journalists and authors with a unique opportunity to see many interesting vehicles and operations in a short space of time. For about ten days each year since 1974 I have been fortunate to attend the September exercise in West Germany. The photographs presented in this volume have been selected from my endeavours of the last eight years and afford the reader an unusual perspective on many of the modern combat vehicles in service with the Allied forces in Europe.

Pierre Touzin, Paris, 1983

2. General Rogers, Supreme Allied Commander Europe.

3. The new American M1 Abrams main battle tank first appeared in West Germany during 1981. The initial arrivals were used for training. The M1 has an 105mm M68E1 gun, the turret for which will be modified at a later date to take the German 120mm smooth-bore gun. A 7.62mm M240 machine-gun is mounted coaxially to the right of the 105mm; another 7.62mm MG is mounted on the top left side of the turret, for the loader; and a 12.7mm Browning M2 HB is mounted by the commander's position. The improved composite armour of the M1 provides protection against anti-tank guided weapons and other battlefield weapons. It is one of the fastest tanks in the world today with an official maximum road speed of about 72km/hr, although it has been reported that the M1 is capable of exceeding 90km/hr.

4. The M551 Sheridan light reconnaissance tank no longer serves in West Germany, the US Army having withdrawn the vehicle from service in 1979. It was unique in that its M81 gun/launcher could fire either the Shillelagh anti-tank missile or a variety of conventional rounds. About 1,700 Sheridans were built.

5. Before being shipped to US units in Europe, the M551 Sheridan was used in Vietnam where it did not prove suitable for the type of warfare fought in that theatre. A .3in M73 machine-gun is mounted coaxially to the main 152mm short gun. The Sheridan is fully amphibious. This vehicle has a flotation screen fitted around the top side of the hull.

6. The M60A1 is the main battle tank of the US Army, which has as its main armament the British 105mm L7 gun (designated M68 in the USA). A .3in machine-gun is mounted coaxially to the left of the main gun. An M85 .5in AA machine-gun is mounted on the commander's cupola.

7. NBC training during Exercise 'Certain Encounter' in September 1981. Various combat vehicles and their crews were decontaminated on the field. This M60A1 is in the hands of an NBC unit. The driver is not wearing a mask but the loader (left side of the vehicle) and gunner are wearing protective masks, probably the ABC-M14A2.

5△

6△   7▽

△8　▽9

8. This M60A1 has been fitted with an M9 bulldozer blade, which is used for preparing fire positions and clearing obstacles. It is also sporting the new US four-tone camouflage pattern. A total of 6,270 M60A1s have been built for the US Army and the Marine Corps.

9. The M60A2 basically consists of the M60 chassis fitted with a new turret armed with the Shillelagh, which had caused so many problems for the M551 Sheridan, fired by the 152mm gun/missile launcher. This gun/missile system proved just as troublesome for the A2; production began in 1966, but it was a full eight years before it entered service, in 1974. A total of 540 M60A2s have been produced.

10. One successful aspect of the M60A2 programme was the new turret, which provided far better frontal ballistic protection.

11. The M60A3 is the latest member of the M60 family to enter service. The main changes to the M60A3 are internal and relate to the fire control system; the A3 has a Laser Tank Fire-Control System (LTFCS), which comprises a laser/sight and a solid-state computer. The most obvious external change visible on this A3 is the thermal sleeve on the gun. Other indicators include the smoke dischargers (covered by a canvas hood here) and the top-loading air filters. The US Army plans to have a total of 3,700 A3s in service by 1985; 1,980 of these would be retrofitted M60A1s and the remaining 1,700 new A3s.

12. The M728 combat engineer vehicle is also a member of the M60 family. It has a hydraulically operated dozer blade mounted at the front of the hull. The turret has been modified to carry a short-barrelled M135 165mm demolition gun and an A-frame jib boom with a lifting capacity of about 11 tonnes. The M728 has a four-man crew. It has a combat weight of 52.16 tonnes.

13. The M728 has the same engine as the M60A1 and M60A2, a Continental AVDS-1790-2A 12-cylinder diesel developing 750bhp at 2,400rpm. The vehicle is used to remove obstacles, dig combat positions, destroy fortifications and recover vehicles. In addition to the main armament, the vehicle has a .3in MG mounted coaxially to the 165mm main gun and a .5in M85 machine-gun in the commander's cupola for ground and AA use. This M728 has an infra-red searchlight mounted above the main armament.

14. Until 1963, when it was replaced by the M60 AVLB, the M48 was used as the chassis for the US Army's standard armoured vehicle-launched bridge. The chassis of the M48 and M60 are virtually identical, the main difference between the two being the engine type.

15. The rectangular plate on the front of the M60 AVLB supports the weight of the bridge during laying down or retrieving operations. The aluminium, scissors-type bridge can be laid in about three minutes and retrieved in between ten and sixty minutes. The combat weight of the M60 AVLB is 55.74 tonnes; without the bridge, the chassis weighs 41.7 tonnes.

16. An M60 AVLB retrieving its bridge during exercises on 16 September 1981. The small fixed bridge has been 'destroyed', according to the exercise umpires, and the fields on either side are water-logged, so this US armoured unit employs an AVLB to bridge the imaginary gap. The M60 AVLB can span a gap up to a maximum of 18.28 metres, thus it is more than adequate for this small stream. It has a maximum load capacity of 60 tonnes.

14△

15△ 16▽

△17 ▽18

17. The M752 launch vehicle is a variant of the prolific M113 family, and is used as an erector-launcher for the Lance battlefield support missile. In this photograph, the rear door of the M752 is open, the missile has been erected by the hydraulically operated ramp and is ready for firing. Lance can carry either a nuclear or conventional high-explosive warhead and has a range of approximately 110km.

18. An M109A1 self-propelled gun ready to go on the field accompanied by two M548 ammunition carriers. (Note the .5in Browning machine-gun mounted on the cargo carrier in the right of the photograph.) The main armament of the M109A1 is a 155mm long-barrelled gun (designated the M185), which has replaced the 155mm 'short' gun on all M109s belonging to the US Army. The combat weight of the A1 is about 24 tonnes.

19. The M109A2 made its first appearance with the US Army in West Germany during 1980. It uses the same long-barrelled gun as the A1, but improvements have been made. The most obvious external differences between the A1 and A2 are the square ballistic shield over the gun sight on the front left-hand corner of the turret, and the increased size of the rear turret bustle, which enables the A2 to carry additional ammunition.

20. In the 1950s, the US Army initiated a programme aimed at providing them with a family of self-propelled weapons that would be air-transportable and share common parts. This project resulted in the M107 self-propelled 175mm gun and the M110 self-propelled 8in (or 203mm) howitzer. Development began in 1969 on a new version of the M110 with a longer range and able to fire new, improved ammunition. It entered service in 1977 and was called the M110A1. The M110A2, which is illustrated here, has the addition of a double baffle muzzle brake and can fire a higher charge than the A1, but otherwise is identical.

21. An M110A2 demonstrates its 54km/hr maximum road speed along a German autobahn, while on its way to take up a new position. The full operating team of an M110 comprises thirteen men.

19△

20△ 21▽

13

22. A basic M113A1 armoured personnel carrier photographed during Exercise 'Certain Encounter' in September 1981. The M113A1 is now the standard production M113. It has a two-man crew (driver and commander) and can carry eleven infantrymen. This photograph affords a good view of the commander's pintle-mounted .5in Browning, for which a total of 100 rounds of ready-use ammunition are carried.

23. This M113A1 was the only one seen with an inscription on the side during Exercise 'Constant Enforcer' in September 1979. The M113 used a Chrysler V-8 petrol engine, but in the M113A1 this was replaced by a General Motors Detroit diesel engine, which increased the operational range of the vehicle from 321km to 483km. This view shows the hydraulically operated ramp at the rear of the hull, which is the entrance and exit for the eleven infantrymen the vehicle can accommodate.

△22 ▽23

24. To obtain an armoured anti-tank vehicle quickly, the US Army mounted the TOW anti-tank system on the M113 APC, developing a retractable M220 mount for the purpose. The interior of the TOW M113 has been reconfigured to accommodate the missile rounds and the M220 mount. No armour protection is provided for the crew, a shortcoming that was remedied later with, first the provision of a Kevlar-armour fabric tent and, later, armoured protection incorporated in the Improved TOW vehicle. The .5in machine-gun on the M113 TOW has a folding mount.

25. The TOW system ready to open fire. The gunner is lining up a target through the sights before firing the missile and guiding it to the target. After launching, the plastic tube that contains the missile is jettisoned. In addition to being vehicle-mounted, TOW can also be used by infantry units and can be air-launched from a helicopter. TOW has a minimum range of 65m and a maximum range of 3,750m.

△26 ▽27

26. US units in West Germany received the M901 ITV (Improved Tow Vehicle) in 1981. The system basically consists of a twin-tube missile launcher mounted on an M113 APC chassis fitted with a new M27 cupola. The two tubes are either side of the sight assembly, and the acquisition sight is positioned on top of the main assembly. Manufactured by Emerson, the system was designed for the M113A1 APC, although it is suitable for several other wheeled and tracked vehicles. The US Army placed an initial order for 1,100 ITVs, which was followed by a second order for 892 systems.
27. An M901 ITV during Exercise 'Certain Encounter', 16 September 1981. The system is in travelling position, retracted into the top of the hull. The elevating mount allows the vehicle to remain hidden while only the launcher and sight assembly are exposed to view. The retracting facility of the launcher mount allows the loader to replenish the tubes from within the vehicle.
28. US M1 main battle tank.
29. US M113A1 armoured personnel carrier.

△30 ▽31

30. British Chieftain main battle tank.

31. British FV432 armoured personnel carrier.

32. Although tanks carry their own anti-aircraft protection, such armament is inadequate against modern aircraft. The M163 Vulcan air defence system was accepted into US Army service in the 1960s to provide AA cover for armoured units. The system illustrated here comprises an M741 chassis (a variant of the M113) with a one-man electrically-driven turret mounting a 20mm six-barrelled M116A1 Vulcan cannon. The fire-control for the system is mounted on the right side of the turret. The United States first took delivery of the M163 in August 1968; final deliveries were made in 1971. There are about 380 M163A1s currently in service with the US Army.

33. The M163A1 Vulcan, shown here in the firing position. The maximum rate of fire of the M61A1 cannon in the anti-aircraft role is 3,000 rounds per minute. The gun can be used in the ground-attack role, when its rate of fire is 1,000 rounds per minute. The maximum effective AA range of the cannon is 1,600 metres, with a maximum ground range of 3,000 metres. The replacement for the M163A1 is the DIVAD (Divisional Air Defence) system, which is expected to enter service in the mid-1980s.

34. The M48 Chaparral low altitude self-propelled surface-to-air missile system consists of a modified M548 cargo carrier, designated M730, mounting a missile launch assembly with four Sidewinder air-to-air missiles modified for ground-to-air missile launch. Individual Chaparral systems do not have their own radar, but it is possible to couple them with a Forward Area Alerting Radar which provides warning of approaching targets. The missiles are not fitted on their launch rails in this photograph, and the launch station is in the lowered position. The six bows stowed on the front of the hull provide the frame for the tarpaulin that covers the rear portion of the vehicle during long journeys. The missile's maximum effective range is 5,000 metres.

32△

33△ 34▽

△35 ▽36

35. The M106A1 107mm mortar carrier is the basic M113 APC chassis with a 4.2inch (107mm) M30 mortar mounted on a turn-table in the rear compartment of the vehicle. Carried externally on the left side of the vehicle is a mortar base plate and bridge, which allow the mortar to be used independently of the vehicle. A 12.7mm M2 HB machine-gun is fitted on the commander's cupola to provide secondary armament. The M106A1 carries 88 rounds of mortar ammunition.

36. The standard armoured command post of the US Army is the M577/M577A1, which is basically an M113/M113A1 but with a higher roof to the rear of the driver's position, and no armament. This view of the diesel-powered M577A1 shows the generator, which provides the power for the extra communications equipment the vehicle carries in the rear compartment, and the tent erected at the rear to increase the work area. A total of 2,693 vehicles have been built for US requirements. Note the MERDC four-tone temperate camouflage scheme on the hull.

37. An M577A1 command post belonging to a US Army decontamination unit at work in September 1981 during Exercise 'Certain Encounter'.

38. The M577A1 command post is also used by artillery fire control units, as here. These crewmen are removing the camouflage net before starting work. Stowed along the track are components used to pitch the tent at the rear. Note the MERDC camouflage scheme on the hull.

△39

△40 ▽41

39. An M113A1 ambulance stands by ready to give first aid, if required, to a company of the US 11th Cavalry as they receive fire drill training, near Fulda, 3 April 1975. When used in the ambulance role, the M113A1 can carry four stretchers.

40. The M548 tracked cargo carrier is used for a variety of roles, including (as here) employment as an ammunition resupply vehicle for self-propelled artillery units equipped with the M109A1 SP gun. A .5in machine-gun is fitted to the M66 ring mount over the top of the cab of this M548. The cargo area is enclosed by a standard vinyl-coated nylon cover. The M548 can carry a maximum load of 5.4 tonnes. The US Army has 3,683 examples of this vehicle.

41. The M578 light armoured recovery vehicle is a variant of the chassis used by the M107 and M110 SP guns. Production of the M578 was completed in the late 1960s, only to be put back into production in 1975 to fulfil requests from the US Army. This M578 is seen in the travelling mode with an M577 in tow. The operator is seen here taking up his position in the turret, which can be traversed through 360°. The driver is seated at the front of the hull on the left side, with the engine on his right. The vehicle has two winches: a tow winch with a maximum capacity of 27 tonnes and a hoisting winch with a maximum capacity of 6.75 tonnes. Other equipment includes tools, tow bars, a hydraulic impact wrench, and acetylene welding and cutting equipment.

42. The M578 has a maximum road speed of 54.7km/hr and is powered by a General Motors Model 8V71T turbo-charged diesel engine developing 425bhp at 2,300rpm. The vehicle has a fuel capacity of 1,135 litres and a range of 723km. The M578 does not have an amphibious capability but can ford up to a depth of 1.06m. The combat weight of the M578 is 24.3 tonnes. Note the tools stowed on the front of the turret.

43. An M88 armoured recovery vehicle, which is the US Army's heavy (50.8 tonnes) ARV, in travelling order towing an M728. The first production M88s were completed in 1961, and used many components of the M48 MBT. The M88 has a hull of cast armour and rolled armour welded together to protect the four-man crew when operating in front-line areas. On the front of the hull is a hydraulically operated blade, which stabilizes the vehicle when the winch is being used and is employed for bull-dozing operations.

44. The M88A1 has a Teledyne Continental Motors AVDS-1790-2DR diesel engine, developing 750hp at 2,400rpm, which has replaced the Continental AVS1-1790-6A petrol engine of the original M88. The diesel engine has increased the range of the vehicle from 360km to 450km, but the maximum road speed of both the M88 and M88A1 is 42km/hr. Above both the engine compartment and the crew compartment is an A-type boom which, with the blade down, has a capacity of 22.68 tonnes. The M88A1 is in production and is expected to remain in service with the US Army into the 1990s. One small feature that can help distinguish between the M88 and M88A1 is the small grille on the right side of the A1.

42△

43△ 44▽

△45

△46 ▽47

45. The British Army no longer uses the Centurion as a main battle tank but finds them ideal for the task being performed by this Centurion Mk. 12, which is seen here as an artillery observation post during Exercise 'Certain Encounter' in West Germany in September 1981. The Mk. 12 has a 105mm L7 main gun to the left of which is a 22in infra-red searchlight.

46. The Centurion Mk. 5 AVRE (Assault Vehicle Royal Engineers) is the only model of the Centurion family that is still performing its intended role within the British Army. It is basically a Mk. 5 but with its original 20pdr replaced by a short-barrelled 165mm demolition gun and a hydraulically operated dozer blade mounted at the front. Above the dozer blade is a fascine cradle, which carries a bundle of wood for filling ditches or lining trenches.

47. A British Army Centurion Mk. 2 armoured recovery vehicle on its trailer during Exercise 'Spearpoint' in September 1980. The vehicle's main equipment comprises a winch with a capacity of 31 tonnes, and two large spades at the rear. A jib crane can also be mounted if required. Usually, the Mk. 2 mounts a .3in (7.62mm) Browning machine-gun and ten smoke dischargers in two groups of five.

48. Until the new Challenger tank enters service, the Chieftain will remain the current main battle tank of the British Army. The armament of this Mk. 3 comprises a 120mm L11A5 main gun with fume extractor and thermal sleeve, a 7.62mm coaxially mounted machine-gun, a 7.62mm machine-gun fitted on the commander's cupola and a 12.7mm ranging machine-gun above the main gun.

49. The British Army ordered 810 Chieftain tanks, all of which were produced between 1962 and 1971. The Chieftain Mk. 5 has a Leyland L60 No. 4 Mk. 6A multi-fuel engine, developing 750bhp at 2,250rpm. The first mark of the L60 engine, which is situated at the rear of the vehicle, was the Achilles' heel of the Chieftain, but development of the component continued and it is now considered much more reliable.

50. The British Army's Chieftain armoured vehicle-launched bridge (FV4205) can carry and lay either a No. 8 or a No. 9 tank bridge. The AVLB seen here during Exercise 'Spearpoint '80' in West Germany is carrying a No. 9. It has a three-man crew.
51. A British Army Chieftain AVLB recovers its No. 9 bridge. This type can span a gap up to 12.2m and has a total roadway width of about 4m; although neither the No. 8 nor the No. 9 bridge takes long to launch (between three and five minutes).
52. A Chieftain AVLB carrying the No. 8 scissors bridge, seen here in company with part of the bridge train – a Ferret liaison and scout car and an FV434 maintenance carrier – during Exercise 'Certain Encounter' in September 1981. The No. 8 can span a gap up to 22.9m. The combat weight of the AVLB with the No. 8 bridge is 53.3 tonnes.

52△

△53 ▽54

53. During 'Spearpoint '80', the biggest British-managed exercise since the Second World War, improvisations with Chieftain tanks such as this were seen. This example has been made to look like a Soviet T62 tank by fitting a dummy minesweeper apparatus on the front of the hull.

54. Each squadron of the British Army's Armoured Regiment has one Chieftain equipped with a dozer blade, which is used to dig defensive positions or to clear routes. The blade is aluminium and operated by the driver, who is seated at the front of the hull. The electro-hydraulic power pack for the dozer blade is positioned on the right-hand side of the hull at the front, in place of the usual stowage bins. The Chieftain has a four-man crew, consisting of a commander, loader, driver and gunner.

55. A Chieftain armoured recovery vehicle (FV4204) uses its

dozer blade to repair the damage caused by a column of tanks during Exercise 'Constant Enforcer' in West Germany in September 1979. The ARV is based on the chassis of the Mk. 5 Chieftain main battle tank. It has two winches: a main double capstan winch that is controlled electro-hydraulically, and an auxiliary, hydraulically operated winch.

56. The commander of this British Army Chieftain ARV is indicating that the vehicle is about to turn left. This tank has a 50.2 tonnes combat weight, a maximum road speed of 41.5km/hr and a range of 320km (roads). The ARV's armament usually consists of one cupola-mounted 7.62mm machine-gun, two mountings each containing six smoke dischargers at the front, and two mountings each containing four smoke dischargers at the rear.

57. The Alvis Scorpion light tank forms the basis of the Combat Vehicle Reconnaissance (Tracked) family of vehicles. The British Army received its first production Scorpions in 1972. The combat weight of the Scorpion is 8 tonnes and its maximum road speed 80.5km/hr. Its armament consists of a 76mm L23A1 gun and a 7.62mm machine-gun mounted coaxially to the left of the L23. The Scorpion (FV101) has a Jaguar J60 No. 1 Mk. 100B spark-ignition engine developing 190bhp at 4,750rpm. Note that the commander (left) and gunner (right), seated in the all-welded aluminium armour turret, each has a hatch cover that opens to the rear, whereas the driver has a hatch cover that swings to the left.

58. The Scimitar reconnaissance vehicle (FV107) is another member of the Scorpion family. The British Army received their first production vehicles in March 1974. The most obvious difference between the Scimitar and Scorpion concerns the main armament:

△57 ▽58

Scimitar has a modified turret mounting a 30mm Rarden cannon. This Scimitar was used by the umpires to follow the armoured units during Exercise 'Spearpoint' in September 1980. After refuelling, the vehicle is ready to go again.

59. It is impossible to tell from this rear view whether the vehicle is a Scorpion or a Scimitar. In fact, it is a Scimitar laden with a variety of equipment.

60. In the late 1950s Vickers started design work on a new self-propelled gun that would use many components of the FV432 APC. The project would comprise a new 105mm gun in a turret with a 360° traverse. The first production Abbot, as the new weapon was called, was completed in 1964, with production ceasing in 1967 after a total of 96 Abbots had been built. The 17km (maximum) of the 105mm gun is insufficient for modern warfare requirements and the Abbot will soon be replaced in British Army service by the new tripartite SP70 155mm self-propelled gun.

59△ 60▽

▽61

△62 ▽63

61. Spartan armoured personnel carrier (FV103) – yet another member of the Scorpion family – entered service with BAOR (British Army of the Rhine) in 1978. The vehicle is crewed by a driver, vehicle commander/gunner and section commander/radio operator and can carry four infantrymen. It can be used in a variety of roles, such as Swingfire re-supply vehicle for the FV438 and Striker launcher vehicles, carrying Royal Artillery Blowpipe SAM teams, and transporting Royal Engineer assault teams. Spartan's armament consists of a 7.62mm machine-gun on the right side of the vehicle commander/gunner's MEL-made No. 16 cupola and four smoke dischargers mounted on each side of the hull at the front.

62. A Spartan APC meets a Scorpion light tank during Exercise 'Certain Encounter' in West Germany, September 1981. Evident in this view are the Spartan's single rear door with integral vision block, the two periscopes on the left side of the vehicle, and two jerry cans in the basket at the rear.

63. The Sultan (FV105) was first delivered to the British Army in April 1977 where it is replacing the Saracen as command vehicle. This member of the Scorpion family has a similar hull to the Samaritan armoured ambulance with the raised roof in the rear compartment, which houses mapboards, radios and other equipment.

64. GKN Sankey built the FV432 armoured personnel carrier for the British Army from 1963 to 1971. The vehicle illustrated is the standard model but numerous variants have been produced. It has a two-man crew and can carry ten infantrymen. This example has a maximum road speed of 52km/hr. The FV432 will be replaced in BAOR by the MCV 80 in the mid-1980s.

65. The FV438 is a variant of the FV432 and is used by the Royal Artillery to mount the Swingfire anti-tank missile system. In this view, the two launcher bins on the top of the hull at the rear are visible, despite the camouflage. Fourteen missiles are carried inside the vehicle, which has a combat weight of 16.2 tonnes.

△66

△67 ▽68

66. A variant of the FV432 being used by the Royal Engineers on exercise in September 1981. It is carrying a variety of equipment, including telephone wires and a ladder. The number 51 on the hull was allocated to the unit for the duration of Exercise 'Certain Encounter'. The number 16 in the white circle gives the combat weight of the vehicle (in tons).

67. The FV432 APC may also be converted into an ambulance. This variant has no armament and carries four stretcher cases or two stretcher and five seated patients as well as a two-man crew. Easy loading and unloading of the stretchers is facilitated by sliding swivel racks.

68. The FV432 is also used by the Royal Engineers on a chassis for the Ranger anti-personnel mine system. The Ranger has 72 disposable tubes, each of which holds 18 mines. The mines can be launched out to a distance of 100 metres. The system's complement of 1,296 mines can be loaded in less than six minutes and, if required, each tube can be fired independently.

69. German Leopard A1A1 main battle tank.

70. German Marder mechanized infantry combat vehicle.

△71 ▽72

73.△

71. German Gepard 35mm AA gun system.
72. US M163A1 20mm AA vehicle.
73. An FV434 maintenance carrier operated by the Royal Electrical and Mechanical Engineers. The main role of the FV434 is to change major components in the field, for which purpose the vehicle is fitted with an HIAB crane with a lifting capacity of between 12.5 tonnes and 30.5 tonnes. The suspension of the vehicle can be locked when the crane is in use. The combat weight of the FV434 is 17.75 tonnes, a little heavier than the

standard FV432 (15.10 tonnes). The hull of the 434 is slightly different to the FV432, especially at the rear which is sloped. The vehicle has a four-man crew.
74. An FV434 at work repairing an FV432 APC. It has removed the 432's Rolls Royce K60 No. 4 multi-fuel engine, to allow the repair team to work on the General Motors Allison TX200 4A transmission. The disabled FV432 is fitted with the Peak Engineering lightweight turret armed with a 7.62mm GPMG and eight smoke dischargers.

74.▽

△75 ▽76

75. Daimler developed the new CVR(W) Fox (FV721) reconnaissance vehicle between 1965 and 1967. The Royal Ordnance Factory, Leeds started production in 1972 and built a total of 230 for the British Army. It is a 4×4 with a combat weight of about 6 tonnes. The armament of the Fox includes a 30mm Rarden gun and a 7.62mm machine-gun mounted coaxially to the left of the main armament. The vehicle has a maximum road speed of 104km/hr and a maximum road range of 434km.

76. The Daimler Ferret scout car has had a long and distinguished career with the British Army and, with the cancellation of its intended replacement, the Vixen, it is expected to remain in service until the 1990s. The first production Ferrets, Mks. 1 and 2, were completed in 1952. By the time that production of the vehicle ceased in 1971, a total of 4,409 examples of all types had been built. The vehicle illustrated is a Ferret Mk. 1/2 (FV704) and is used by infantry units as a light reconnaissance vehicle. The usual armament of the Mk. 1/2 is a 7.62mm pintle-mounted Bren light machine-gun. The vehicle has a three-man crew.

77. A rear view of a Ferret Mk. 1/2 in a West German town during Exercise 'Spearpoint '80'. The Ferret has a Rolls Royce B60 Mk. 6A petrol engine developing 129bhp at 3,750rpm. It has a maximum road speed of 80km/hr and a maximum road range of 306km.

78. A simulated nuclear attack during Exercise 'Spearpoint '80'. The Ferret Mk. 2/3, which is a later production model of the basic Mk. 2, is not fitted with an NBC (Nuclear, Biological and Chemical) system. This crewman is wearing defence clothing and has an S6 respirator. The combat weight of the Mk. 2/3 is approximately 4.4 tonnes and it has a two-man crew.

'**79.** Exercises in West Germany are very realistic. This Ferret Mk. 2/3 has been concealed in a barn during 'Spearpoint '80', a favour that the farmer concerned will be paid for. This vehicle has a turret-mounted .3in Browning machine-gun for which a total of 2,500 rounds of machine-gun ammunition are carried.

77△

78△   79▽

△80 ▽81

80. The Alvis Saracen FV603 armoured personnel carrier was one of the first models in the post-war FV600 series of 6×6 vehicles. The Saracen was the standard APC of the British Army in the 1950s and early 1960s until replaced from 1963 by the FV432. A total of 1,838 Saracens were built and the type is still in service with the British Army reserve units and several overseas armed forces. Saracen has a small turret similar to that fitted in the Ferret Mk. 2/3, armed with a .3in Browning machine-gun. Note the ring mount on the roof at the rear, which is usually fitted with a 7.62mm Bren light machine-gun or a .3in Browning. In

addition to the two-man crew, the vehicle can carry ten infantrymen.
81. Some reserve British Army units also participated in Exercise 'Spearpoint '80', bringing their own vehicles with them, including Saracen armoured personnel carriers. The Saracen shown here is the ambulance variant FV611, which has no armament. In addition to a two-man crew, the vehicle can accommodate ten seated patients, or three stretcher and two seated patients, or two stretcher and six seated patients.

82. The British Army has a special combat engineer tractor (FV180) designed to provide engineer support for units near the front line. A total of 141 CETs have been built for the British Army, which uses them for a variety of purposes. The equipment it carries includes a hydraulically-driven capstan winch, a light alloy bucket with a steel cutting edge for digging or bulldozing, and a self-emplacing earth anchor that can be rocket-propelled out to a distance of 91.5m. The FV180 has a two-man crew and a combat weight of 17.1 tonnes.

83. The CET is one of the vehicles used to tow the Giant Viper anti-tank mine-clearing equipment, which is a trailer-mounted, rocket-propelled, explosive-filled hose for clearing a route through a minefield. The FV180 has a Rolls Royce C6 TFR diesel engine developing 320bhp at 2,100rpm. Its maximum road speed is 56km/hr. The CET is fully amphibious and is propelled in the water by two Dowty water jets, providing a maximum swimming speed of 5 knots.

82△ 83▽

△84

84, 85. The Leopard 2 is the newest and most powerful tank in the inventory of the West German Army. Manufactured by Krauss-Maffei, the Leopard 2 has a combat weight of about 55 tonnes. It has an MTU MB 873 – Ka 501 engine which develops 1,500bhp at 2,600rpm. Its maximum road speed is 72km/hr. The tank's armament consists of a 120mm main gun, a coaxial 7.62mm machine-gun and a 7.62mm AA machine-gun. The Leopard 2 is now in production and it is already in use with some German units. The example in **85** is shown on trials in Switzerland.

86. A total of 1,845 Leopards were built in the first four production batches, an example of which is seen here during the 'Schneller Wechsel' exercise in September 1974. Although the

▽85

retrofitting of these vehicles into Leopard A1s had already begun by this time, the Leopard illustrated is still in its original form. The tank's armament consists, like all the A1 to A4 models, of the British 105mm L7A3 gun (also used by the British Centurion, the US M1 and US M60, among others) and a coaxial 7.62mm machine-gun. A second 7.62mm machine-gun, intended for anti-aircraft defence, can be seen on the turret roof.

87. This Leopard A2 has a reinforced cast steel turret, rubber pads to protect the tracks and a thermal sleeve around the main gun. A total of 232 A2s were built for the West German Army. The apparatus on the main gun in front of the fume extractor is a gunfire simulator used during exercises. Note the Alouette II helicopter in the background.

△88

88. The Leopard A3 and A4 differ from the A1 and A2 variants in that they have a welded turret of spaced armour with a wedge-shaped mantlet. A total of 110 A3 vehicles were produced for the Bundeswehr. The A4 was the last production model of the Leopard built for the German Army, which bought 250 of them. The A4 model (shown here) is similar to the A3 but has an integrated fire-control system, which consists of a stabilized panoramic telescope for the commander, and a computer-controlled rangefinder, coupled to the fully-stabilized main armament and ballistic computer. The Leopard variants share the MTU MB 838 Ca M500 10-cylinder multi-fuel engine, which develops 830bhp at 2,200rpm. The maximum road speed is 62km/hr.

89. The large and numerous forests in West Germany provide ideal cover for armoured units, which can move along the forest paths without fear of air attack. The Leopards that were uprated to A1s in 1971 were modified again in the late 1970s with the fitting of spaced armour to the turret and mantlet, and called the Leopard A1A1. The box-like device on the mantlet of this A1A1 is a searchlight.

90. This Leopard A1A1 almost plunged into an open drain during a cross-country manoeuvre. The driver turned the vehicle sharply to avoid the obstacle but broke a track in the process. Support in the shape of a Leopard armoured recovery vehicle was soon on the scene to provide assistance. The blackened grille on the side of the Leopard A1A1 is one of the vehicle's two engine exhausts.

89▽ 90△

△91 ▽92

91. The Gepard is a self-propelled anti-aircraft gun system and a member of the Leopard family. The system's main armament consists of two Oerliken 35mm KDA cannon, which are mounted externally on either side of the turret. Each barrel has a cyclic rate of fire of 550 rounds per minute. Gepard has a pulse-doppler search radar mounted on the rear of the turret, and a pulse-doppler tracking radar mounted on the front of the turret. The range of each is 15km.

92. The search radar of this Gepard is seen here in action. Manufactured by Siemens, the search radar rotates at 60rpm and provides surveillance of air space out to a range of 15km. It has an IFF (Identify Friend or Foe) capability which, when not required, can be folded down behind the rear of the turret. A total of 432 Gepards were built for the Bundeswehr by Krauss-Maffei.

93. The Bundeswehr requested a special version of the Leopard tank to provide on-the-spot repairs or, failing that, tow disabled vehicles to a repair depot at the rear. Production of the Leopard armoured recovery vehicle, as it was called, was undertaken by MaK of Kiel. A total of 444 ARVs were built for the West German Army, which also has 100 product-improved versions of the type.

94. The Federal German Army's engineers needed a special tracked vehicle that could accompany the armoured units through the battlefield. A version of the Leopard tank based on the ARV was built by MaK for this purpose and called the Leopard armoured engineer vehicle. The first production vehicles were completed in 1968. Among other roles, the vehicle is used to remove obstacles or to dig combat emplacements. A total of 36 AEVs are in service with the Bundeswehr.

95. A Leopard ARV at work during Exercise 'Certain Encounter' which was held in the area of Frankfurt-am-Main in West Germany in September 1981. The recovery vehicle is using its crane to remove the armour plates from the rear deck of a Leopard with engine trouble.

93△

94△ 95▽

96. In Europe there are many natural obstacles for tanks to cross, such as ditches and rivers. Many of them are not very wide or deep, but they are sufficient to halt the passage of armoured units not equipped with bridging equipment. The Brückenlegepanzer Biber, or armoured bridgelayer, based on the chassis of the Leopard MBT, provides this support for the West German Army, which has 105 of these vehicles in service. Built by Krupp MaK, the first production models were completed in 1975.

97. A Leopard bridgelayer minus its bridge tracks a Unimog 1300L 4×4. Biber has a cantilever-type bridge of aluminium construction which can span a gap up to 20m. It is unusual in that it lays its bridge horizontally not vertically, which allows bridgelaying operations to be completed unobtrusively. The combat weight of the vehicle with the bridge is 45.3 tonnes.

△96　▽97

48

98△ 99▽

98. The German Army bought US-built M48 tanks, such as this M48A2, until its own industry could start home production. This model has a 90mm gun, a 7.62mm coaxial machine-gun and a 12.7mm anti-aircraft machine-gun. Its combat weight is 47.6 tonnes.
99. A total of 650 M48A2 tanks have been retrofitted by the Germans and given the designation M48A2GA2. The main modifications visible in this photograph are the British 105mm L7 main gun; the new mantlet supporting a searchlight; and the new cupola fitted with the German MG3 machine-gun. The Leopard is slowly replacing the A2GA2s.

△100

100. The Jagdpanzer Rakete self-propelled ATGW vehicle entered production in 1967 and succeeded the Jagdpanzer Kanone. The Rakete mounts two launchers for the French Aérospatiale SS-11 wire-guided ATGW (retracted in this view), a 7.62mm MG3 machine-gun on the right side of the vehicle and, if required, a second 7.62mm MG3 for AA use. The vehicle carries fourteen missiles and 3,200 rounds of ammunition. Eight smoke dischargers are mounted on the roof.

101. This photograph provides a good view of an SS-11 on its launcher, ready to fire. The missile's minimum range is 500m and

it has a maximum effective range of 3,000m. The two launchers are used alternately: while one missile is guided onto its target, the second launcher arm is retracted into the vehicle and reloaded. The Rakete has a combat weight of 23 tonnes. Its Daimler-Benz MB 837 8-cylinder water-cooled diesel develops 500hp at 2,000rpm. Maximum road speed is 70km/hr. A total of 370 vehicles were built for the German Army, the majority of which are retrofitted with the new HOT ATGW system and additional armour.

▽101

102△

102. The German Army used many self-propelled anti-tank guns during the Second World War with great success. The idea was re-adopted by the Bundeswehr later and a chassis was developed that formed the basis of the Jagdpanzer Kanone (seen here) and the Jagdpanzer Rakete. The main armament of the Kanone is a hull-mounted 90mm gun. Secondary armament consists of a 7.62mm MG3 machine-gun mounted coaxially with the 90mm gun and an additional 7.62mm MG for anti-aircraft use. Apart from the Belgians, who have their own Kanone variant, the West German Army is the only force with which the vehicle is in service. A total of 770 have been built for the Bundeswehr.

103. The M109 self-propelled gun was developed for the US Army and first entered service in 1963. The Bundeswehr has bought nearly 600 M109s, which are designated M109G in the West German Army. The M109G differs from the US model in several respects. The combat weight of the 109G is 24 tonnes and its maximum road speed is 56km/hr.

104. The M107 175mm self-propelled gun is also US made. The 175mm M113 gun fires an HE projectile weighing 66.78kg to a maximum range of 33km, depending on the type of charge used.

103△ 104▽

△105   ▽106

105. The Marder is the mechanized infantry combat vehicle of the German Army. Production was split between Rheinstahl (later Thyssen) and MaK (later Krupp MaK) with over 3,000 vehicles being built between 1970 and the completion of production in 1975. The Marder's combat weight is 27.5 tonnes and it has a maximum road speed of 70km/hr. The vehicle has a four-man crew and can accommodate six infantrymen in its compartment at the rear.

106. The primary role of the Marder is to provide infantry support for the Leopard tanks. The MOWAG-designed remote-controlled 7.62mm MG3 machine-gun positioned at the rear of the hull is shown clearly in this view. The vehicle's complement of six infantrymen enter and exit via the power-operated ramp at the rear.

107. This close-up shows in detail some of the Marder's impressive weaponry. The vehicle's main armament is a 20mm Rheinmetall Mk. 20 Rh202 cannon, which is fed from three different belts, allowing the gunner to select the ammunition appropriate for each target; for example, AP for armoured vehicles and HE for softer targets. Some Marders, such as this example, were equipped with a mounting for the Milan ATGW system.

108. The West Germans use the Marder chassis to mount the Euromissile Roland 2 surface-to-air missile system. The first Roland unit was delivered to the Bundeswehr in 1978. The Roland 2 consists of two launchers, pulse-doppler surveillance radar and a tracker with two guidance modes, optical or radar. The missile has a maximum range of 6.3km and a minimum range of 500m. It is a low-altitude system, designed to deal with enemy aircraft flying between 20m (minimum altitude) and 5,000m (maximum altitude).

109. The American M113 family of APCs, built by FMC, is used widely by the West German Army. Several versions of the M113 have been developed by the West Germans to fulfil their particular needs, including this M113A1 artillery observation post vehicle.

107△

108△   109▽

△110 ▽111

110. The West German Army has about 500 M113A1 mortar carriers in service. The carrier is fitted with a Tampella 120mm mortar, which fires to the rear of the vehicle. Although it has an amphibious capability, when afloat the carrier's total capacity of 63 120mm mortar bombs has to be reduced to 23. There is a ramp at the rear of the vehicle for loading and unloading the mortar. Note the 7.62mm NATO G3 rifle slung on the inside of the door.

111. The M577A1 is the command post variant of the M113 family. Basically, it is an M113/M113A1 with a higher roof extending from behind the driver's position. When the vehicle is stationary, a tent can be erected at the rear to provide more space.

112. The M113A1 is unarmed when used as an ambulance. Its basic task is to transport the wounded from the battlefield to a field hospital. A high percentage of

112△

113△ 114▽

the casualties these men would have to transport from the scene of a real tank battle would be suffering from burns.

113. The French Hotchkiss series formed the basis of a complete family of light tracked vehicles adopted by the Bundeswehr in the late 1950s. The variant seen here is the SPz 11-2 reconnaissance vehicle, known as the Aufklärungspanzer Schützenpanzer Kurz in the West German Army. The SPz 11-2 has a three-man crew and is armed with a Hispano-Suiza HS 820 20mm cannon. The Luchs (8 × 8) has now replaced the SPz 11-2 in German front-line service.

114. The SPz 2-2, or Krankenpanzer KrKw gep, is another member of the Hotchkiss family. The weight of this vehicle is 8 tonnes. In addition to the three-man crew, it can carry two stretcher and one sitting patient inside the vehicle, with a further two stretchers on the roof.

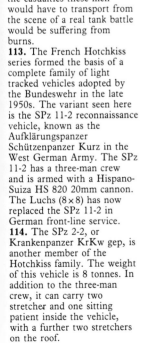

△115

△117

115. The Bundeswehr bought the Lance surface-to-surface missile system from the USA. The launcher vehicle for Lance in West German service is the M548 chassis, which works in conjunction with the M688 (illustrated), the loader/transporter for the system. The M688 carries two Lance SSMs and is fitted with a hydraulic crane (seen here extended) for loading the missiles. The Lance missiles in German service are not fitted with nuclear warheads.

116. The Transportpanzer 1 (6×6) armoured amphibious load carrier was one of the vehicles to emerge from the development project for a new range of military vehicles instigated by the Federal German Defence Ministry in 1964. The TPZ1 is built by Thyssen Henschel, who delivered the first of the 996 vehicles on order for the Federal German Army in 1979. Transportpanzer 1 has a combat weight of 17 tonnes and a maximum speed of 105km/hr.

117. The Spähpanzer Luchs is the Federal German Army's latest armoured amphibious reconnaissance vehicle, the first example of which was officially handed over to the Army in September 1975. The vehicle has the twin advantages of excellent cross-country mobility and quietness. The armament of the Luchs is obscured by camouflage in this view, but it consists of a 20mm Rheinmetall Mk. 20 Rh202 cannon and a 7.62mm MG3 machine-gun for both ground and anti-aircraft defence. The Rheinmetall TS-7 turret has spaced armour for increased protection. The Luchs is fully amphibious and is propelled in the water by two Schottel steerable propellers fitted on either side of the hull at the rear. This heavy (combat weight, 19.5 tonnes) has a crew of four.

118, 119. The first production examples of the 110mm Light Artillery Rocket System (LARS) were delivered to the German Federal Army in 1970. A total of 209 LARS are in service with the West Germans, who are expected to replace the system with the US MLRS in the mid-1980s. The LARS consists of a truck chassis with an armoured cab and a multiple rocket launcher at the rear. The launcher for the LARS has two units, each with eighteen barrels. The system has a maximum range of 14km. In illustration **118** the system is seen mounted on a Magirus Deutz (6×6) 7,000kg Jupiter lorry, while in **119** it is mounted on the MAN 6×6.

▽116

118△ 119▽

△120 ▽121

122△

120. Belgium was the first NATO country after West Germany to order the Leopard, its first order for the Leopard I being placed in 1967. 334 examples of the type have been bought. The Belgians mount an FN 7.62mm machine-gun instead of the original German 7.62mm Rheinmetall machine-gun. The Leopard I shown here does not have the spaced armour on the turret and mantlet of the later variants. It is also without side skirts.

121. A Leopard AEV of the Belgium Army with its crane elevated. The Belgians have ordered 36 of these vehicles to accompany their Leopard MBTs.

122. In October 1970 the Belgian Army placed an order for 701 Alvis CVR(T) Scorpions. The first deliveries were made in February 1973. The crew of three comprises a driver (whose compartment is at the front on the left), a commander (seated in the turret, on the left) and a gunner (seated in the turret, on the right). The Scorpion has an all-welded Alcan aluminium armour, as do all the models of the CVR(T) series.

123. At the end of Exercise 'Constant Enforcer' in September 1979, this Belgian Scimitar reconnaissance vehicle remained concealed in a farm until the command was given to return to barracks. First deliveries of the Scimitar were made to the Belgian Army in April 1974. The Scimitar has the same hull and turret as the Scorpion but, instead of mounting the 76mm L23 as its main armament, it has the 30mm Rarden cannon. In addition to the Rarden, the Scimitar also mounts a 7.62mm machine-gun, coaxially to the left of the main armament, and four smoke dischargers either side of the front of the turret.

123▽

124. A Belgian Spartan (FV103) armoured personnel carrier, September 1979. The basket on the rear door provides storage space, below and to the left of which is a thread roller for a field telephone. The combat weight of the vehicle is 8,172kg. Spartan has an amphibious capability, and when used in this mode the tracks act as propellers. Note the flotation screen around the top of the hull.

125. The Sultan armoured command vehicle (FV105) is a member of the Scorpion family with a hull similar to that of the Samaritan. This rear view of a Belgian Army Sultan gives some idea of the paraphernalia of equipment the vehicle carries. The command area is restricted to the rear of the vehicle but can be extended by erecting a tent, seen here folded on the roof. Sultan normally carries at least two radios (one at the front and one at the rear), and mapboards. The vehicle's armament consists of a pintle-mounted 7.62mm machine-gun and four smoke dischargers mounted on either side, towards the front.

△124 ▽125

126. The AMX VC1 armoured personnel carrier, which was developed by the French in the early 1950s, is still used by the Belgian Army. The vehicle carries a total of thirteen men. The concept behind the design was that, apart from the driver, all personnel could exit the vehicle and be used in the combat role. AMX VC1s in Belgian Army service are fitted with a Browning machine-gun instead of the original 7.5mm MG used by the French.

127. The Belgian Army is the only armed force in the world to retain the American M75 armoured personnel carrier, over 1,700 of which were built by International Harvester between 1951 and 1954. When the type was finally replaced in US service by the M59 in the late 1950s, the remaining M75s were transferred to the Belgian Army. The vehicle's long service with the Belgians will come to an end soon, however, with the first delivery of its replacement, the FMC A1FV. The M75 has a two-man crew and can carry ten infantrymen. Its armament consists of a pintle-mounted 12.7mm M2 HB machine-gun.

126△ 127▽

△128 ▽129

128. The Canadian Army replaced their Centurion tanks with a modified version of the Leopard 1A3 fitted with the Belgian SABCA fire control system. This version is called the C1 by the Canadians. So far, Canada has bought 114 C1s, a number of which are based in Europe. The C1 illustrated here was taking part in an exercise in West Germany in September 1978, three months after the Canadians had received their first delivery of the type.

129. Optional equipment for the Leopard includes a complete dozer blade unit. The Canadians placed an order for these after experimenting with the vehicle over rough terrain in Canada. Production started in 1978. The entire dozer blade can be either attached or removed in about ten minutes without resort to a recovery vehicle or crane.

130. The Canadian Army has also bought eight Leopard armoured recovery vehicles, which are production-improved models developed and built for the Federal German Army by Krupp MaK. The Germans took delivery of their 100 production-improved Leopards in 1978.

131. The Canadians have six Leopard bridgelayers, which are identical to the model used by the West German Army. The weight of the bridge and vehicle together is 46 tonnes. When extended, the bridge can span a gap up to 20 metres.

130△ 131▽

△132

132. Artillery units are the most difficult to spot during exercises because they are so well camouflaged and spend most of the time in static positions. The only areas that are visible on this Canadian Army M109A1 self-propelled howitzer are the muzzle brake of the 155mm gun, the turret hatches and the 12.7mm machine-gun. The basic differences between the M109 and the M109A1 variants are the latter's new and longer barrel, designated M185.

133. The Lynx (or M113) armoured command and reconnaissance vehicle, which is manufactured by FMC, is used only by the Canadian and Netherlands armies; in Canadian service the vehicle is called the Lynx, but the Dutch call it the M113 C and R. The first of the 174 Lynx for the Canadian Army were completed in 1968. The Canadian Lynx weighs 8.8 tonnes and has a GMC Detroit Diesel 6V53 engine which develops 215hp at 2,800rpm. The vehicle has a three-man crew. The large cupola houses the commander, who also operates the 12.7mm machine-gun. The optional secondary armament, a 7.62mm machine-gun,

is usually mounted by the observer's hatch, which is to the left and slightly behind the commander's position. This Lynx is unarmed; note that even the smoke discharger dispensers are empty.

134. A Canadian M113 mounting the US TOW (Tube-launched, Optically tracked, Wire-guided) system. The M220 TOW Launcher is very similar to the infantry version used on the ground. In addition to TOW, the vehicle is mounting a Browning machine-gun. The two vertical steel bars at the front of the vehicle are to protect the driver from decapitation should any wires be stretched across the vehicle's path.

135. A Canadian M113 APC fitted with a hydraulically operated dozer blade, which enables the vehicle to carry out general bull-dozing work, improvement of water entrances and grading. Behind the driver is an air vent for the engine. The large door at the front allows access to the engine compartment. The weapon mounted at the commander's position is a .3in Browning machine-gun.

▽133

△136 137▽

136. The Canadian Army uses the M806 recovery vehicle, which is basically an M113A1 with a hydraulic winch and a fairlead assembly for retrieving disabled vehicles. This rear view shows the vehicle's spades, which are mounted either side of the ramp and are lowered during recovery operations. A third, auxiliary spade unit is carried on the roof. The winch is carried inside the h

137. A convoy of Canadian M548 tracked cargo carriers passes through a village in West Germany in September 1979. The M548 is yet another member of the M113 family. It is unarmoured yet fully amphibious and can carry 5.5 tonnes of carg

138. The Royal Netherlands Army is not a regular participant in the big NATO exercises. This photograph shows an M109A1 self-propelled gun of the 44th Field Artillery Battalion taking part in the 'Carbine Fortress' exercise in September 1982. This unit comprises three gun batteries equipped with M109A1s. In the near future the Royal Netherlands Army will receive the new M109A2 as a replacement for the A1.

139. The Dutch have their own version of the M901 ITV fitted on the Armoured Infantry Fighting Vehicle (AIFV), which they have designated YPR-765 PRAT. This vehicle is fitted with the Emerson ITV turret. The Royal Netherlands Army has ordered 850 AIFVs from the American manufacturer FMC. This Dutch Army YPR-765 is seen on display at the international air show in France, June 1981.

138△　139▽

△140

△141 ▽142

140. The Netherlands Army has adopted the Leopard tank for its armoured units. A total of 468 Leopard A1A1 are in use. Some specialized versions of the Leopard family were also ordered by the Dutch. The version illustrated here is known as 'Caesar' and is an anti-aircraft vehicle fitted with a twin 35mm gun. The main difference between this vehicle and the Gepard is that Caesar has a Hollandse Signaalapparaten radar system. The Royal Netherlands Army has a total of 100 Caesars. (Netherlands Army)

141. The new M110A2 self-propelled gun, which is produced by Bowen-McLaughlin York in the United States, has also been adopted by the Dutch. The M110A2 is an improved version of the M107 and M110 SP guns. The gun is a 203mm with a long barrel and a muzzle brake. (Netherlands Army)

142. The FMC M113 C and R used by the Royal Netherlands Army differs from the Canadian model, with the driver and observer seated side by side in the front of the combat room. A total of 250 have been purchased by the Dutch. (Netherlands Army)